I healed myself the way I show in the book (Lupus). I taught my children and they do the same. My grandchildren are learning now.

Twenty-two years ago I had the idea to write the words, did the first rendition of Bernie and Babs, and put down a storyboard. Nine months ago while transferring my art cabinet to the new studio (I am a painter by trade) that work fell out in the yard. My new adopted dog grabbed it and brought it inside and put it on my lap. Since then every time I let it fall aside, a sketch or painting falls off a table or wall to the ground. I have no credentials to validate my knowledge or the vision of this book. I do have the unwavering knowing that it will help heal millions if not billions. Our minds are miracles we have yet to tap to the fullest. This book is a step toward that.

– Grandma Ness

BERNIE AND BABS vs THE VIRUS

Adventures in Healing

Grandma Ness

AUSTIN MACAULEY PUBLISHERS™
LONDON • CAMBRIDGE • NEW YORK • SHARJAH

Ordering Information
Quantity sales: Special discounts are available on quantity purchases by corporations associations, and others. For details, contact the publisher at the address below.

Publisher's Cataloging-in-Publication data
Ness, Grandma
Bernie and Babs vs the Virus

ISBN 9781649795526 (Paperback)
ISBN 9781649795533 (Hardback)
ISBN 9781649795557 (ePub e-book)
ISBN 9781649795540 (Audiobook)

Library of Congress Control Number: 2022903141

www.austinmacauley.com/us

First Published 2022
Austin Macauley Publishers LLC
40 Wall Street, 33rd Floor, Suite 3302
New York, NY 10005
USA

mail-usa@austinmacauley.com
+1 (646) 5125767

Inspiration was received from my daughters, Journey Neveah and Miranda Fast, by growing up and using these bugs and bots to heal themselves. Further and indispensable inspiration and creativity came from Alex Boger, Ayalesse Fast, Xomara Fast, and Kimber Fast, the world's most wonderful amazing grandchildren. Bill Morrison who is my best friend and partner in any adventure in this world told me to do it, listened and suggested when it was needed. He inspires me to believe in myself every day. I love you all.

I would love to acknowledge Lynette Christensen for her expertise in children's books as our local children's library aficionado. She was an amazing editor and content voice in refining this work into a good and coherent piece of literature. She took the book and, for free, blessed me with notes and potential corrections. Her detailed viewpoint was invaluable. Hope Hooper was one of the few adult beta readers and she was very instrumental in a few different stages on her feedback in a very usable way. Also, the amazing team at Austin Macauley Publishers who took an unknown author and jumped in to create an up-to-date and inspirational book that I am sure will be a standard for ages.

Into every child that is born
Hides a gift, to heal they are sworn
Noble and brave, they come to your call
That is all it takes, that is all.

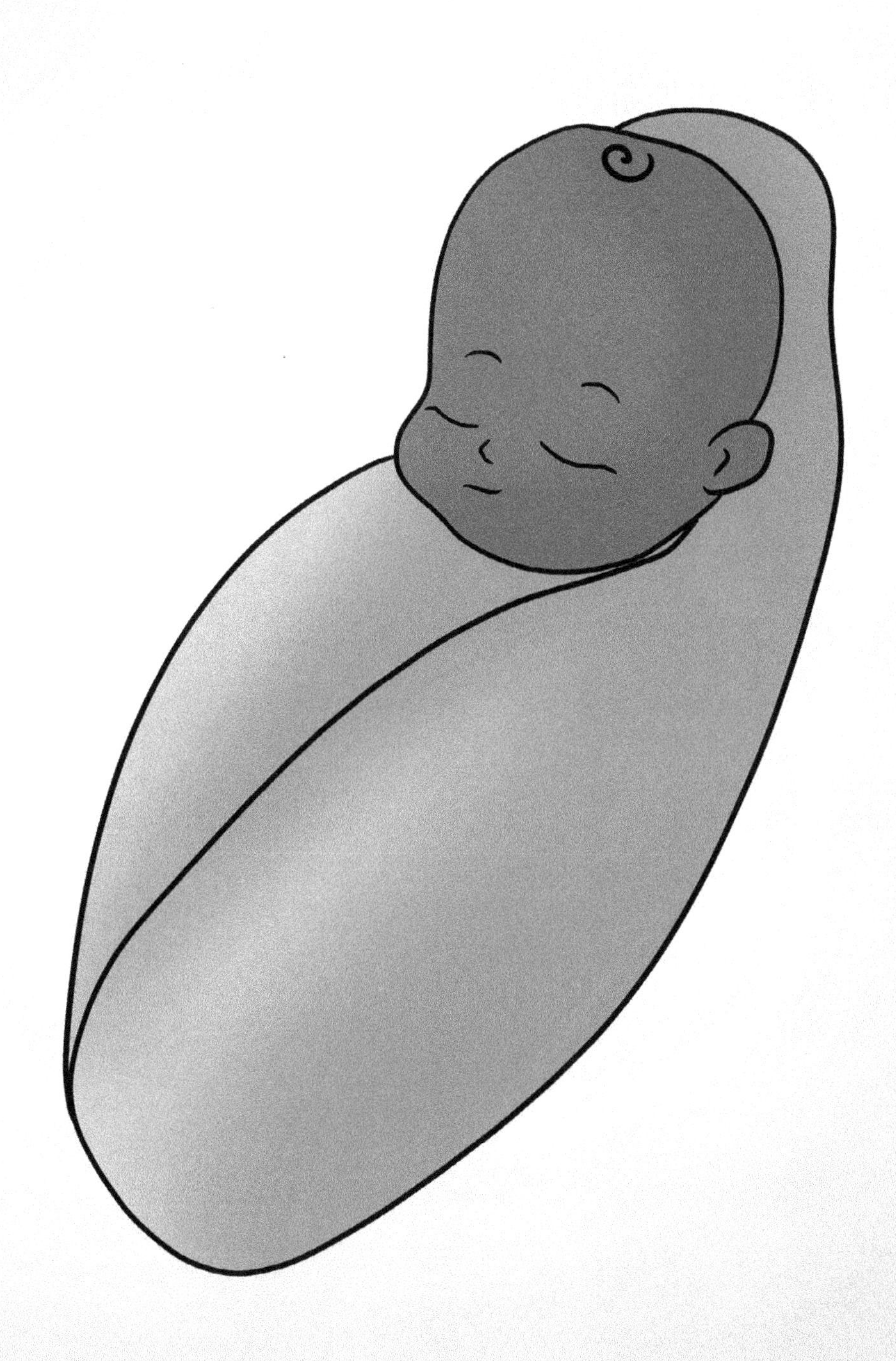

Feeling icky and run-down

You must go into town

See the doctor and find out why

Doctors know, doctors try.

Doctor Checklist
Fever
100.3
Clammy
allover
Tired
Runny Nose
Icky Throat
VIRUS
Send out bugs and bots

Way down deep, deep in the gray

Where the clacking clacks, and
thinkings play
The control center of all that you are
Is taking in messages, is sending them far.

When there is trouble and something
is wrong
Alarm bells will ring, sirens, horns, and gongs
Who do they tell, to whom can they shout
Bernie and Babs, we need you:

come out!

No matter where, no matter when
Bernie Bugsley hears and calls all his friends
Into a line they come, come in a clatter
Grabbing trusty buckets and magic hammers

Together they march, march with great haste

Soon they arrive at the trouble place
Green goopy monsters, good turned bad
Building their owies, creating saddest sads.

Forward fearless undaunted they come
Bucket to shields like inside-out drums

Hammers flail wildly, baddies are stunned
They catch everyone, even those that runned.

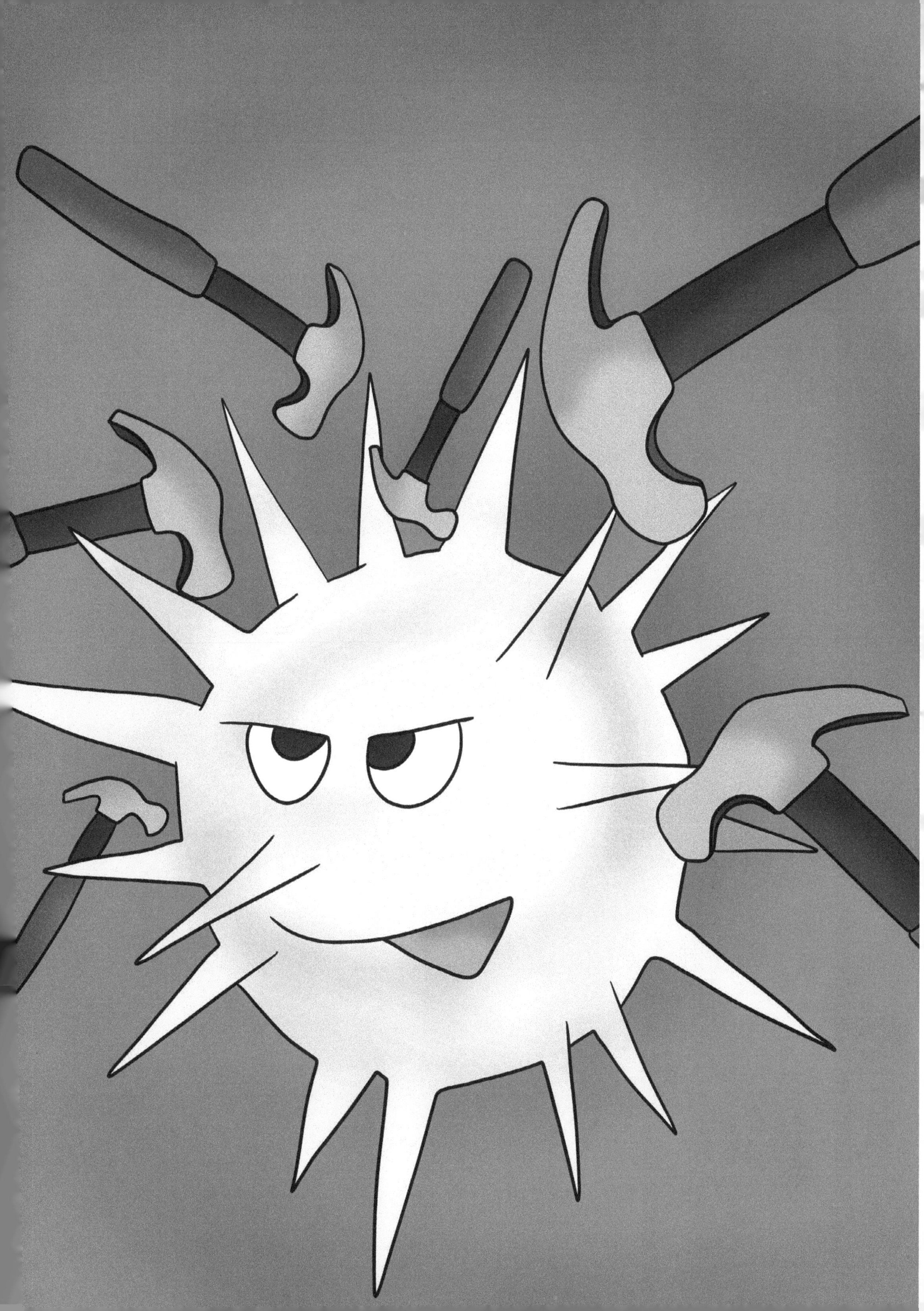

Jiggle and flip,

trusty turn of the hip

Shields turn buckets to catch every drip

Load and stack to carry away

Buckets full they walk from the fray.

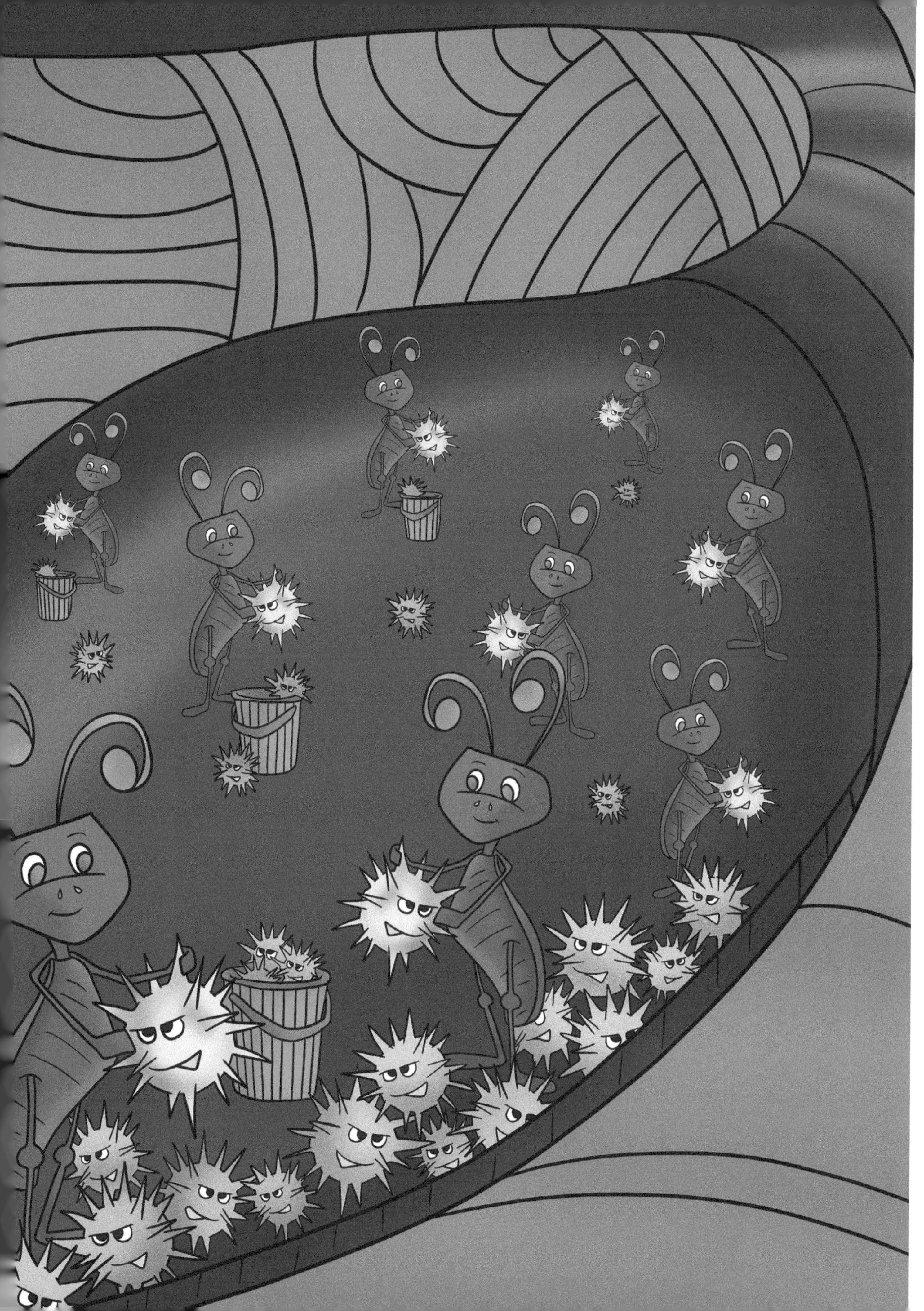

Dumping the junk,

as great dumpers do
Into the rivers that clear all the goo
So when you go, out it will flow
Flushed to the place where baddies
can't grow.

Baddies gone but, oh what a mess
Who will clean this scene of distress?

Fiddle, faddle, sort, and plot

Babs the Bot Queens map the spot
Figure how many for quick repair
Then send them quickly there.

Babs the Bot Queens turn limbs down
To repair and stitch the broken ground
As they repair, they start to hummm

Babses like making work more fun!

Back at Babs activity room
They're planning the fix for the doom
Planning doesn't stop at fixing. Oh no
They must find where defenses are low.

Many other Babses traveled elsewhere
The source is in need of repair

Meticulous they sort through every bit
To find the DNA that allowed it.

"I found it!"

yelled Babs. "Send location to mind."
Energy signals relay the find.
Screens all find that tiny spot
Then it's reprogrammed by the Bots.

Oh what a party, what laughter, what joy
The foe is vanquished,
hurrah hurroy!
So when you feel icky, or poo poo, or down
There's no cause to whimper,
whine, or frown
You have the power to put out the call
Then in your mind you can picture them al
The Bernie Bugslies will clear it all out
And the Babs the Bot Queens fix
it throughout.
You are the master, you sound the call
The hero is you after all
Will you feel better, oh yes for real
You have bugs and bots to command,
HEAL!

CPSIA information can be obtained
at www.ICGtesting.com
Printed in the USA
BVHW021214030522
635995BV00048B/2342